Healthy Living

THE SECRET
INGREDIENTS

'Food and Medicine come from the same source'

W0010930

Contents

Healthy Living: 'The Secret Ingredients'

Healthy Ingredients:

The nutriton information is based on the *Food Composition Database* of the Japan Science and Technology Corporation, Japan.

Note: If you have any health problems consult a medical or nutrition specialist. This book is not to replace any current or future treatment, care or advice. The author and publisher hereby disclaim responsibility for the results of anything following or not following the information given in this publication.

Introduction

The World Health Organisation (WHO) recently announced its results for its 191 member countries regarding the number of years they can expect to live in good health. The US ranked very low, 24th in the global list and the UK managed only 14th place, whilst the Japanese ranked 1st with their average healthy life expectancy now at a remarkable 74.5 years. Their total life expectancy is obviously an even greater figure, and what most are now interested in, are not only ways to increase longevity but to further improve health alongside it.

The WHO's figures show that Japanese healthy longevity is closely linked to the traditional Japanese diet. There is concern that the major changes in recent eating habits, chain smoking and high alcohol consumption will compromise these figures in future. From the early '60s the rate of animal fat consumption in Japan rose dramatically and so too, cholesterol levels. Comparisons

made with
increase in

threefold increase amongst women. In the last 50 years stomach, colon, pancreatic, lung, uterine, prostate and kidney cancers have all shown alarming increases; chronic heart disease has increased similarly. Japan has also seen an incredible rise in the severity of menopausal and post-menopausal symptoms. It is quite clear that the generations born prior to the '60s are those to look to as a model for a lifestyle of 'healthy' longevity. But even those earlier generations famously worked unbelievably long hours, spent far above average time commuting and took painfully short holidays, yet overall they somehow still live the longest, healthiest lives. The question is, how ?

A look at the roots of the traditional Japanese diet will provide an historical and philosophical background to their longevity. Examining how dietary requirements are balanced with what nature has to offer, and developing a greater aesthetic and spiritual appreciation of food and surroundings, will help to draw links with how the Japanese achieve their enviable state of health. Improved stamina, healthy looking skin and increased longevity can all be enjoyed as the just deserts of improved diet.

History

An introduction to the history of Japanese cuisine
& its inextricable relationship with good health.

Start with the Sea

Historically, the Japanese looked to the islands' natural resources
for their food, relying heavily on the abundant sea stocks, on
hunting, and on harvesting and gathering the many varieties of
seaweed, mountain vegetables and herbs.

Rice culture was introduced to Japan from either China or Korea
after 300BC. Well suited to the climate and soils, rice has been
a natural choice as a consistent healthy dietary element.

Soba noodles, again believed to have originated in China, were
adopted into Japanese cooking in the first century AD. These
buckwheat noodles are common ingredients in the Japanese

diet as are the thicker wheat flour noodles *udon*, which are served in healthy soups.

Exposure to Buddhism during the sixth century was instrumental in changing the face of the Japanese diet, and it then gained a more vegetarian accent.

Between the seventh and ninth centuries, many elements of Chinese culture were introduced to Japan and these were to change hitherto traditional farming and cooking methods. Between the seventeenth and mid-nineteenth centuries, the last period of Shogun rule, Japan had further integrated the earlier culinary influences of China and Korea and those of the Westerners who'd ventured that far, mainly as traders and missionaries. These Western influences were largely Dutch, Spanish and Portuguese and brought about the surge in the consumption of meat and dairy products. After the Second World War, Japan looked to the American diet as a source of strength and vigour and further promoted meat, breads, pastries and milk. This was followed by the inclusion of frozen and highly processed instant foods, and as Japan faces increases in heart disease and some cancers these Western fast foods and dairy products are now brought into question.

Fashionable Food

Exporting and importing foods and fashions in dining has obviously been going on for centuries. Countries adapt various foreign dishes to their own tastes and at the same time pride themselves when the traditional or original cuisine is reasonably well replicated, again this is nothing new. But perhaps what is interesting is what happens when a country rediscovers its own food, having tried and tested foreign fare only to find that the recipes from home feed not only the stomach, but health and spirit to boot. It is Japanese cuisine that can rightly lay claim to providing meals that delight the eyes and palate, and stimulate health and well-being at one and the same time.

It is widely believed that importing Western foods, the move towards over-eating, and the over consumption of alcohol are responsible for the marked increases in Japanese health problems. The incidences of cancer of the large intestine, stomach, oesophagus, prostate, breasts and uterus are of particular concern, as are the increases in heart disease and weight problems.

Now Japan's health conscious are assessing the nutritional value of this international-fusion come *con-fusion* diet. Just as Japan imported the hamburger as a trendy fast food, Europeans and Americans have imported sushi and other Japanese foods as the latest in both fashion and healthy eating. And now Japan is reappraising its own cuisine as the latest culinary fashion but more importantly, as highly nutritional food and as a means of guarding against sickness.

Taste of Time

Many ingredients have withstood the tests of time and become essential to the Japanese kitchen. True to its eclectic nature, Japan adopted various tastes from overseas to complement its own, and the healthiest of these became strong features of the Japanese diet. The fermented bean paste, *miso* was introduced from China in the seventh century, and is used widely in Japanese dishes; it aids digestion and helps the body rid itself of toxins. Around the same time, tofu was also adopted, low in calories and high in protein and vitamins this is a perfect food for the weight conscious.

Shoyu "soy sauce" is another familiar Japanese ingredient but rather younger than its miso and tofu cousins, dating back only as far as the seventeenth century. Shoyu is beneficial in relieving tiredness, aids digestion and is rich in B vitamins.

Konbu "kelp" has been used in Japanese cuisine since the first century, and - as is true of all seaweed, is full of vitamins and minerals. It has various properties that help to enrich the blood and aid the body rid itself of impurities.

Fast Food

Since the emphasis in traditional Japanese food is on seasonal foods freshly prepared, many Japanese recipes are quick and easy to make. In that sense, traditional Japanese foods contain the 'speed' element that many rely on with highly processed, Western fast foods.

In Japanese cooking, great emphasis is placed on retaining the natural flavour and texture of ingredients, so it has always been important not to overcook. This style of cuisine leaves the nutritional content intact, and when certain foods are combined these nutritional values are often even enhanced.

The movement in Japan, *back to basics* if you like, means that the complementary ingredients are also re-engaged and appreciated for their restorative or health promoting natures. The vinegar used in fresh sushi preparation has antiseptic and antibacterial properties, and is believed to lower the risk of high blood pressure. With the soaring popularity of sushi, the Japanese themselves are at the sushi bar in ever spiralling numbers, and in this too-fast world, healthy 'fast food' has to be a wiser bet. The West seems eager to continue this trend, and Japanese style bento lunch boxes, with a varied and balanced menu, now regularly outsell their sandwich competitors.

Philosophy

A healthy mind resides
in a healthy body.

Part of the Whole

Modern day medicine relies heavily on science and technology for diagnosis and treatment of illness. Symptoms, ailments and diseases have gradually become isolated from the larger context of an individual's total health. This compartmentalising of the elements of both health and illness has led in part to the divorce of the individual's responsibility from their own well-being, and to the disempowering of people with regard to their own health. Although there is a place for modern medicine there is no need to exclude the foundations of natural healthy living and drawing on food as a natural source of vitality and remedy.

Both good personal conduct and personal responsibility are deeply held Japanese principles. Further developing knowledge of your own health, weak points, predisposition and needs, and beginning to accommodate these as part of your daily routine is incredibly empowering as you slowly improve your general well-being.

Food is Medicine

The basic premise of Japanese healthy living is that healthy food is also the most natural medicine, *Ishoku Dogen* "Remedies and food come from the same source." That there is a close connection between 'healthy body & healthy mind' is a popularly held belief and most certainly originates in the East. The Japanese have long lived by the following idea: *Kenzen na tamashii wa kenzen na karada ni yadoru* "a healthy spirit lives in a healthy body", and perhaps nowhere in the world is it more actively and sincerely pursued than in Japan. The relationship between food, good health and remedy is woven into many cultural and philosophical aspects of Japanese life, so much so that healthy eating habits are quite simply a 'way of life'.

Seven Gods

Some ingredients are celebrated for more than just their nutritional or healing properties. They are thought to encourage positive effects on other aspects of life, and to some degree to feeding the spirit as well as the body.

There's an age old Japanese belief that every grain of rice has seven gods, and leaving any literal interpretations aside, the foundation for this is that each and every grain of rice is of value and at its most basic, is an argument against wasting food.

The Japanese don't traditionally indulge in over-eating and at home are encouraged to revere nature for its part in food provision, thereby being neither greedy nor wasteful of what is available.

There is an inherent cultural relationship that links food, nature and god or gods —depending on each family's belief system— but common to all is the correlation between what you eat, the natural world, the seasons and good health.

Seven Herbs

Nanakusa "Seven spring herbs/vegetables"

From the fourteenth century seven particular ingredients were gathered and included in a dish called *nanakusa-gayu* "seven-herb porridge." This was eaten on the day before the start of spring to encourage the family's good health. The seven special ingredients are: dropwort - Japanese parsley, shepherd's purse, cottonweed, chickweed, henbit, turnip and *daikon* "Japanese radish". This tradition is continued today, occasionally the ingredients will vary by region but are basically the same as those used more than six hundred years ago.

Spring sees the arrival of many new herbs and wild vegetables and the fresh young buds are particularly sought after. The herbs and vegetables will have profited from the nutrients held into the soil by the heavy snows. Following the harsh winter months, the new seasonal plants are the first to experience the benefits of the year's new sunshine. Grazing on these fresh new ingredients takes full advantage of these nutrients and sunshine, encouraging the feeling of consuming fresh new energy and of promoting the same in your own health.

Tradition

Following Japan's old calendar, there are particular days set aside to celebrate the coming of each season. The most beneficial foods and herbs that are freshly available are enjoyed on these special days to promote the family's health. Just as *Nanakusa*'s seven plants and herbs celebrate the emergence of spring, *Doyono Ushinohi* is the day that marks summertime and the traditional food on this day is eel. The summers in Japan can be unbearably hot and humid and this often leads to a poor appetite. Despite the fact that eel is high in fat and calories it is also rich in protein, and consumed in even small amounts provides substantially in terms of nutrition and energy. This makes eel an invaluable food at a time when many people really don't feel like eating a great deal but are working as hard as at any other time of year and require great energy resources.

Shoku-yoku no aki, refers to autumn as the 'season of appetite,' and unlike the other seasons doesn't single out particular foods, as this is the time of year when foods are most plentiful and when the greatest variety can be found. In Japan, autumn is thus quite appropriately thought of as the season that promotes a good, healthy appetite.

As in many parts of the world, New Year's Eve is one of the traditional celebratory days in Japan. And as many parts of the country have particularly harsh winters, any time devoted to enjoying the season is especially welcome. It is therefore on New Year's Eve that people enjoy a dish called *Toshikoshi Soba*. This buckwheat noodle is eaten to celebrate life and wish everyone a long life as they cross between one year into the next. It is a way of hoping for a healthy long life, for good family relations, long friendships and relationships.

In Japan it isn't too difficult to trace the relationship between food and the many roles in which it is employed, and then to link this with the general feeling and atmosphere of good will that seem to provide the context for its appreciation.

The Four Seasons

How to balance your nutritional requirements
with what nature makes available.

The Japanese rely heavily on their diet to help balance the effects
of the changes in weather and temperature, and fortunately
many of the foods and herbs that are seasonally available, meet
these requirements.

Spring

Spring sees the inclusion of butterbur, young
bamboo and many fresh green herbs in Japanese
cooking, all of which promote good health as
people adapt to the changes in temperature
and weather moving from winter into spring.

Summer

In summer, cucumber and Japanese aubergine become popular and these have a cooling effect on the internal organs. Tofu and noodles are more often served cold in summer, accompanied by light meats and fish for sustenance.

Autumn

In autumn the rice is ready for harvesting and mushrooms abound; shiitake is the best known Japanese mushroom and is highly regarded for its health properties especially in terms of cancer prevention.

The persimmon fruit also come into season in autumn and these are very rich in vitamins. As their colour reflects the time of year, persimmon are often included as a decorative element in addition to their great taste and vitamin content. Aesthetics and taste are thus connected to the season alongside the ingredient's health properties, making any such food completely 'whole and harmonious' in the Japanese sense, and such integration is highly regarded.

Winter

There is a whole tradition of one-pot cooking that serves to nourish and warm in the long winter months, especially in the north of Japan subject to extended and particularly mean winters. Various onions and Japanese leeks are used for their ability to help maintain body heat.

Pumpkin are rich in vitamins A and C; they keep well during winter and are invaluable during this season when there are less varieties of fresh fruit and vegetables available.

In Step with Nature

Buying food on a daily basis helps ensure that ingredients are fresh, and traditionally this allows people to choose from those vegetables seasonably available. But with the onslaught of genetically modified foods, nature's rule has been thrown rather off balance. To some degree, the individual is having to remember what 'ought' to be available if they are to have any chance of pursuing a diet with a close link to its original source, environment and cycle. It is these natural cycles of seasons, weather and life that the Japanese seek to preserve, in the belief that intervention or interference in one may lead to adverse effects in the others. This means that people try and consume what is naturally in season, that way the soils and labour replenish at a rate both in step with human requirements and as nature permits.

Mirror of the Seasons

No one really doubts that the seasons and weather affect us and that our moods often reflect them; in general that's fine when it's sunny, but there are times when it is necessary to balance out the more negative conditions. Long dark winters often lead to a feeling of lethargy, lower moods and deficient energy and stamina levels. At these times it is best to compensate for these negative feelings and mirror the season less accurately.

Just as spring provides a more harmonising effect on the natural and human environments after winter, people must likewise assume some of the responsibility for this balancing act, particularly during hard winters or too powerful summers. In effect there should be a pull towards mirroring harmony, and when one aspect is out of step with this, then another should attempt to realign things.

In Japan during the winter months, families and friends will gather together for *nabemono*, one-pot dishes that can include tofu, meat, mushrooms and seasonal vegetables. These ingredients will compensate in some measure for that which is lacking in the weather, and the communal eating encourages a feeling of community and raises people's spirit during the darker, lonelier winter evenings. It is not only necessary to be responsible for eating the most beneficial foods, but to combine it with other needs such as that of companionship at times, and equally of allowing yourself time alone at others. There is the requirement of a certain level of self-awareness, so that each person gauges their own needs at any particular time and seeks to remedy them if necessary, and to do so by themselves as far as possible.

Human Cycle

In terms of general well-being, the Japanese believe that mental as well as physical health will be more consistent if it is allowed to follow natural routines or patterns. This includes eating a healthy diet in measured amounts, at regular times of day so that the body is nourished and energy is replenished in readiness for the next action. What is also important is that each person shows their commitment to what they have set out to achieve, whether these goals be large or small is immaterial, but whether they are completed is crucial. The argument for this tenacity in human behaviour is that it mirrors nature, and just as nature has its own cycles that must be followed and completed before moving on, so too must humans complete their own cycles in order to feel useful and in harmony with their environments.

Environment

The importance of living
in harmony with your surroundings.

Simple Harmony

In the sixteenth century, the tea master Sen no Rikyu developed
a particular style of cuisine called *chakaiskei* to accompany the
tea ceremony. *Chakaiseki ryori*, combined something of the
moderation and essence of Zen with the formal presentation
and etiquette of the *honzen ryori*, which was an adaptation of
the earlier court style of banqueting. His inclination was towards
the use of simple utensils, decoration and settings, and he
preferred the use of natural materials. A modest area of tatami
mats provided the setting and the room was kept relatively
bare, save for a few well chosen objects such as a bamboo vase

and the rough *raku* ware tea bowls. The intention was to create a space that linked with the outside and with nature in an almost seamless connection. He celebrated the use of the ordinary and unpretentious to demonstrate the commonplace aspect of tea making and drinking, and both his style of tea ceremony and his sense of aesthetics have been highly and broadly influential. Nowadays minimalism is still the preferred style for Japanese dining, whether traditional or modern. Incorporating the right decorative elements is also encouraged and people take great pride in fitting their rooms with simple but beautiful objets d'art. The often rustic appearance of the ceramics favoured by Sen no Rikyu allowed the food, tea and flowers to take the foreground. These ceramics used originally as a display of material modesty, now often have great monetary value, and whilst that is indicative of the dualities present in Japanese culture, the associations of humility, good taste and an affinity with nature are all still fundamental to the setting for Japanese cuisine.

I Want To Be Alone

The Japanese are most often described in terms of group culture, but the historical maxim is one of 'being in harmony' and that includes being in harmony with nature and with dietary needs as well as with people.

There are always times when people eat alone but in a Japanese sense, if the individual takes care in choosing their environment and meal, this can be perfectly enjoyable. The company of nature and good food are coupled to feelings engendered by the surroundings, indulging in reflections, memories or plans, and all at your own pace.

The Company of Friends

Japan has a tremendous number of festivals for celebrating food and nature, from 'cherry blossom viewing' in spring to 'moon viewing' in autumn or New Year's celebrations. The ambitious aim is to stimulate all the senses... with ingredients that evoke the season, with the colours, images, textures and flavours co-ordinated to reflect the time of year, and this in the company of friends, in a setting that enhances the moment. When all of these features come together, the Japanese ideal is attained. Whilst ideals often remain distant, perhaps it is enough to be reminded of the elements that create a truly satisfying meal, and to aspire to the same.

Longevity

The rewards of healthy eating:
long life, healthy looking skin, and strong motivation

Certain plants and vegetables have an incredible range of properties, and those included here are ones most closely linked with the secrets of Japanese healthy long life.

Longevity

The many varieties of seaweed are rich in calcium, iron and minerals and as such are wonderful for improving the health of ageing teeth and bones, and for encouraging good circulation. Gingko nuts, rich in carotene, vitamin C, calcium and iron increase both vigour and longevity. Pumpkin is a common ingredient in the Japanese diet; it encourages vitality and healthy skin and helps the body rid itself of impurities.

There are particular illnesses associated with ageing, and pumpkin has been found to be very useful in helping the treatment of some of the most troublesome of these including prostate trouble, diabetes and kidney problems.

Those suffering from heart disease might look to including garlic and sea vegetables in their diet as these work towards reducing cholesterol, and have strong healing properties.

Drawing on various ingredients can soothe menopausal and post-menopausal symptoms, spinach, tofu and lotus root are particularly beneficial.

Power and Motivation

For anyone suffering restless nights, including garlic and pumpkin in your diet can help.

Ginger and shiitake mushrooms help to calm nervousness, they work to decrease apathy and increase energy. Azuki beans also fight tiredness whilst millet is successful in promoting mental agility.

Beauty

Feeding and cleansing the skin from the inside is far more beneficial than creams on the outside or '*modern cuts,*' and there are many ingredients that can be used. Buckwheat, daikon, mushrooms and onions are all very good for keeping the skin healthy, as are soya beans in their various forms, especially tofu. *Hato mugi* "Job's tears" are very highly regarded for their kind effect on the skin and are useful in dealing with skin problems such as eczema, moles and warts.

For anyone worried about greying hair, it is necessary to choose ingredients that promote good circulation, for example, sesame and seaweed. Improving circulation will also help those suffering hair loss. Seaweed is wonderful for the skin and hair, and even increases sexual vitality.

Relax

That's an order!

It sounds too obvious, but how many of us really take enough time to sit and relax when we eat. Long term, eating on the run, at the desk and at lunch meetings, takes its toll. The body needs a certain amount of time and composure to properly digest food, and eating in any state of agitation prevents the body from making best use of food. Poor conditions for the body to digest food include tiredness, stress and other emotional states. It's worth remembering that too much emotion of any kind is believed to have negative effects on the body; again the Japanese look towards moderation in terms of retaining a level of harmonious good health, so relax...

The Japanese Way

Healthy Ingredients

This section of the book explores the health promoting properties
of ingredients commonly used in the Japanese kitchen.

Daikon	Miso
Renkon	Soba
Umeboshi	Genmai
Gobo	Nuka
Shiitake	Azuki
Nira	Goma
Shiso	Konbu
Yamaimo	Wakame
Konnyaku	Nori
Daizu	Hijiki
Tofu	Komezu
Natto	Ryokucha

DAIKON

— Japanese Radish —

Good digestion

Heartburn
Stroke prevention
Nasal inflammation
Digestion
Arteriosclerosis

BASICS Digestion and Congestion

Daikon is particularly beneficial in treating digestive problems and very congested lungs, coughs, colds and flu. It is rich in vitamin C, and promotes the digestion of carbohydrates, which makes it easy on the stomach and good for avoiding heartburn. The skin of the daikon is also good for strengthening the capillaries, and so helps to prevent strokes.

NUTRITION & HEALING Painless Joints

The juice of daikon is good for treating spots and can be applied directly. Soaking a dressing or towel in daikon juice and placing it on the affected area can ease painful joints. For nasal inflammation, simply soak a tissue in the juice and place it gently inside the nostril.

TASTE & USE

The Remedy Radish

Parts of the daikon range from having quite a mild flavour to a rather bitter radish taste. The best time to buy them is between early autumn and early spring. Choose those which still have leaves and which are heaviest, these will be the freshest and contain the most juice. To keep them: remove the leaves and wrap in newspaper or clingfilm, this is to prevent the radish from drying out. They can be kept in the fridge.

FACTS

per 100g DAIKON

Vitamin C	15.0mg	Dietary fibre	1.2g
Calcium	30.0mg	Fat	0.1g
Calories	18.0kcal	Glucose	3.4g
Carbohydrate	4.0g	Iron	0.3mg
Cholesterol	0.0mg	Protein	0.8g

Japanese Radish with Miso Sauce
furofuki-daikon

Slice the daikon, 3cm, cover with water in a pan, add the kelp and simmer for appox.15min - until tender. Mix the sauce ingredients in another pan and bring to the boil. Discard the kelp; serve the daikon on small plates and pour the sauce over them. *Side dish.*

Ingredients (Serves 4)

⅔ daikon
1 sheet kelp
(10cm × 10cm)

Sauce
60g red miso
2 tbsp sugar
3 tbsp *dashi*
2 tbsp *mirin*

*mirin = sweet cooking sake
*dashi = Japanese soup stock

RENKON

Lotus Root

Sexual health and longevity

Longevity
Healthy skin
Stomach & bowel trouble
Menopause
Sexual Health

BASICS

Sexual Health

Renkon has long been associated with increasing sexual health and with healthy longevity. The sticky part of renkon contains a stimulant that helps increase stamina, both physical and emotional. It contains a high amount of vitamin C, sufficient to meet the adult daily requirement. It promotes general good health and healthy skin. It can be beneficial in alleviating menopausal symptoms, irritability and encourages sound sleeping patterns.

NUTRITION & HEALING

Kick Constipation

The high vitamin C content decreases the cholesterol level and promotes good use of dietary fibre. Renkon is rich in dietary fibre making it ideal for treating constipation, stomach ulcers and duodenal ulcers. Drinking the juice of renkon will reduce fever if you have a cold or flu. Dried renkon powder taken with water, can stop hiccups.

TASTE & USE

Rounded Renkon

Renkon have a subtle fresh flavour, the best season to buy them is autumn. Choose the more rounded ones, plump and shiny are the key words here. The tannin content makes the root look black when sliced, so put it in water with a drop of vinegar before cooking to help it retain its pale colour. Try to avoid over cooking renkon or they lose their crispness and much of their vitamin content.

FACTS

per 100g RENKON

Vitamin C	55.0mg	Dietary fibre	2.5g
Calcium	18.0mg	Fat	0.0g
Calories	66.0kcal	Iron	0.6mg
Carbohydrate	15.7g	Potassium	470.0mg
Cholesterol	0.0mg	Protein	2.1g

RECIPE

Simmered Lotus Root

renkon-no-nimono

Slice the lotus root to reveal its floral impression, 1cm, and simmer in the soup stock for 10min. Add the sauce ingredients and simmer for a further 5min. Garnish with sesame seeds. *Side dish.*

Ingredients (Serves 4)

1 lotus root
240ml *dashi*
1 tbsp white sesame
seeds

Sauce
4 tbsp soy sauce
2 tbsp *mirin*
2 tbsp sake

*mirin = sweet cooking sake
*dashi = Japanese soup stock

UMEBOSHI

Pickled Plum

Fight fatigue fast

Food poisoning
Hangover
Fatigue
Appetite stimulant
Flu

BASICS

Fight Fatigue

Umeboshi contain a lot of citric acid, which aids the absorption of carbohydrates and fats, this allows the best use of the energy value of other foods and therefore fights fatigue. These pickled plums have very strong antibacterial properties making them a helpful choice for anyone who is a victim of food poisoning. Umeboshi have been used to treat many conditions for centuries, and over time more and more of their beneficial properties have been discovered. The plums are also useful in treating menopausal symptoms and preventing haemorrhoids.

NUTRITION
& HEALING

Life after Hangover

Umeboshi contain an acid that stimulates liver function, making it a particularly effective ingredient for those recovering from a hangover. It can be useful in treating colds and flu; simply grill a plum until slightly burnt, add hot water, mix, and drink - add honey to taste. These plums are also good for preventing and counteracting travel sickness.

TASTE & USE

Palatable Plums

Umeboshi have a sharp sometimes tart taste and are often rather salty. They are exceedingly good for cleansing the palate and stimulating the appetite at the same time. They should be stored in a cool, dark place that avoids sunlight. If the plums are pickled without any unnatural preservatives they will keep for up to a hundred years. In Japan it is thought that an umeboshi a day helps keep the doctor away.

FACTS

per 100g UMEBOSHI

Vitamin C	0.0mg		Dietary fibre	4.4g
Calcium	24.0mg		Fat	0.8g
Calories	39.0kcal		Glucose	9.8g
Carbohydrate	11.1g		Iron	1.7mg
Cholesterol	0.0mg		Protein	0.8g

RECIPE

Rice Ball
onigiri

Cook the rice. Wet the palms of your hands and rub lightly with salt. Spread the rice in the palm of one hand, make a hollow in the centre for the umeboshi and enclose it, making a triangular shape. Wrap seaweed around the rice. *Light dish.*

Ingredients (Makes 1)

1 umeboshi (stoned)
80g rice
1/8 sheet *nori-*
(2.5cm x 19cm)
salt

*nori = sheet dried seaweed
(1 sheet - 21cm x 19 cm)

GoBo

Burdock Root

Goodbye to bowel trouble

Bowel cancer
Constipation
Diabetes
Arteriosclerosis
Urinary infection

BASICS

To Sit !

Gobo is very high in dietary fibre, which keeps the bowels in good working order, and in healthy condition. This ingredient is helpful in treating all manner of bowel disorders and haemorrhoids. It is beneficial in preventing cancer, especially of the bowel; it also promotes stamina and helps cleanse the body of infections of the urinary tract.

NUTRITION & HEALING

Remove Toxic Waste

If you simmer the root in water, the water makes a very useful remedy as well as the vegetable itself. Eaten and drunk together, they aid digestion, and have properties to remove toxins from the body, making them useful in cases of food poisoning. Gargling with the simmered water is good for mouth ulcers, and the juice of gobo counteracts insect bites and stinging nettles when applied directly.

TASTE & USE ## Gobo & General Health

Gobo have a tendency to taste quite bitter. Soak in vinegared water before cooking to prevent loss of colour. The best season to buy them is autumn. Choose the straightest you can find, without cracks in the skin and ideally those that are still muddy; avoid hairy ones, as these are old. If you want to store them, leave the mud on, wrap them in newspaper and leave them in a cool, dark place. As this vegetable has such great cleansing qualities it promotes general physical good health.

FACTS

per 100g GOBO

Vitamin C	4.0mg	Dietary fibre	8.5g
Calcium	49mg	Fat	0.1g
Calories	76kcal	Glucose	16.2g
Carbohydrate	17.6g	Iron	0.8mg
Cholesterol	0.0mg	Protein	2.8g

RECIPE

Julienne Burdock
kinpira-gobo

Shave cut the burdock root and carrot, rinse and drain. Slice up the chilli and stir-fry in sesame oil, add the burdock and carrot and cook for 5min. Add the sauce and cook until the sauce is reduced to nothing. Garnish with sesame seeds. *Side dish.*

Ingredients (Serves 4)

150g burdock root
50g carrot
2 tbsp sesame oil
½ red chilli

Sauce

50ml soy sauce
1 tsp sugar
2 tbsp sake

some sesame seeds

Shiitake Mushrooms

Assist in cancer prevention

Arteriosclerosis
High blood pressure
Weight control
Phlegm
Cancer

BASICS

Cancer Protection

Shiitake have anti-carcinogenic properties and are therefore a good food to include in the effort to prevent cancers. These mushrooms have long been used in Chinese medicine to help cleanse the blood, and are useful in the treatment of arteriosclerosis and high blood pressure. They have almost no calories, which makes them suitable for those watching their weight, and have been of benefit to sufferers of liver conditions and in reducing phlegm.

NUTRITION & HEALING

Lower the Pressure

Shiitake are a very rich source of vitamins B and D; dried shiitake have obviously had greater exposure to the sun and this means their vitamin D content is even higher. Vitamin D aids the absorption of calcium which stengthens bones and teeth. When consumed with asparagus, the effectiveness of the shiitake doubles – especially in the treatment of high blood pressure and arteriosclerosis.

TASTE & USE

Shiitake Shine

Shiitake are the most popular mushrooms in Japan. They have a strong distinctive flavour and are quite 'meaty,' and this makes them a substantial addition to any meal. The best seasons to buy shiitake are spring and autumn; it is best to choose shiny, plump looking ones with short stems. Store them in a dry place, as they will easily go off in the damp.

FACTS

per 100g SHIITAKE

Vitamin B₁	0.07mg	Carbohydrate	6.2g
Vitamin B₂	0.24mg	Cholesterol	0.0mg
Vitamin D	90.0IU	Dietary fibre	4.1g
Calcium	4.0mg	Iron	0.4mg
Calories	18.0kcal	Protein	2.0g

RECIPE

Rice & Mushrooms
shiitake gohan

Remove the stems of the mushrooms, slice and rinse them. Slice up the deep-fried bean curd. Mix the soup stock, soy sauce, sake and mirin together and then cook the mushrooms, bean curd and rice in this in place of water. *Main dish.*

Ingredients (Serves 4)

300g shiitake mushrooms
450g rice
4 slices deep-fried
bean curd

600ml *dashi*
3 tbsp soy sauce
1 tbsp *mirin*
1 tbsp sake

*mirin = sweet cooking sake
*dashi = Japanese soup stock

NiRA

— Garlic Chives —

Correct body temperature

Cold
Flu
Poor circulation
Diarrhoea
Constipation

Body Heat

Nira are very good at regulating body temperature and as such are good at treating poor circulation, stomach problems, both diarrhoea and constipation. During periods of cold weather, these garlic chives are very effective in retaining body heat and are good for people suffering from colds or flu. Nira have a high vitamin B_1 content and help the body retain its vitamin B_1, and that is wonderful for stamina and helps in the recovery from fatigue.

Immune System Booster

These chives also contain a lot of carotene, which converts to vitamin A, helping to boost the immune system. They are beneficial to those suffering from a bad stomach and in counteracting morning sickness; for these conditions you can mix the juice of the chives with milk, or milk and honey and take it as a drink. The juice can also be used directly on bruises or chilblains.

TASTE & USE

Autumn Chives

Nira's taste and smell is not dissimilar to that of other chives though they are perhaps slightly more pungent. The best time to buy these chives is between mid spring and mid autumn. Choose those that are the brightest green and that have a strong smell. Nira don't keep very well, so once you've bought them try and use them within two days. The vitamin A content is increased when the chives are cooked in oil so stir-frying seems an obvious cooking method.

FACTS

per 100g NIRA

Vitamin A	1800.0IU	Calories	19.0kcal
Vitamin B1	0.06mg	Carbohydrate	3.7g
Vitamin B2	0.19mg	Dietary fibre	2.0g
Vitamin C	25.0mg	Iron	0.6mg
Calcium	50.0mg	Protein	2.1g

Egg with Garlic Chives
nira no tamago toji

Slice the garlic chives, 4-5cm. Boil the soup ingredients, add the chives and simmer until cooked. Beat the eggs and pour them over the soup. Place the lid on the pan and simmer until the egg is half cooked. *Side dish.*

Ingredients (Serves 4)

300g garlic chives
4 eggs

Soup
120ml *dashi*
1 tbsp sugar
1 tbsp soy sauce
1 tbsp sake

*dashi = Japanese soup stock

SHISO

Beefsteak Plant

Sleep easy

Insomnia
Allergies
Immune system
Food poisoning
Diarrhoea

BASICS

Sleep Easy

It might sound like something of a contradiction, that this plant at once promotes restful sleep and at the same time is thought to have properties that are refreshing and revitalising, but that is the case. The Chinese characters for this plant actually mean 'revive/revitalise' and whilst this is one of their properties, it also promotes a healthy appetite and aids restful sleep at night.

*NUTRITION
& HEALING*

Soothed Skin

Shiso contain a lot of vitamins and minerals and are a good boost to the immune system; they are particularly good in helping treat skin conditions and allergies, and have a general health promoting and soothing effect on the skin. These leaves have strong antibacterial properties making them effective against food poisoning, diarrhoea, colds and flu.

TASTE
& USE

Summer Leaves

The taste and aroma of shiso is something akin to that of basil and mint. They are best bought between early summer and early autumn. Choose smaller leaves as the larger ones will be older and therefore less fresh. Choose the brighter green ones, which are more aromatic. Shiso increase in potency when cooked in oil, so like the Japanese garlic chives, are a good option for stir-frying. These leaves are often eaten with *sashimi* (raw fish) and sushi because of their antibacterial properties as well as for their aroma and taste.

FACTS

per 100g SHISO

Vitamin A	4800.0IU	Calories	35.0kcal
Vitamin B₁	0.12mg	Carbohydrate	7.0g
Vitamin B₂	0.32mg	Cholesterol	0.0mg
Vitamin C	55.0mg	Iron	1.6mg
Calcium	220.0mg	Protein	3.8g

RECIPE

Shiso Parcels
shiso no hasami age

Knead the chicken well with salt and pepper. Take 1 tbsp of chicken and spread it evenly on the surface of one leaf, sandwiching it with a second leaf. Mix the egg, water and flour, dip the shiso and chicken parcels in this batter and then fry them in vegetable oil. *Side dish.*

Ingredients (Serves 4)

16 shiso leaves
200g minced chicken
salt & pepper

½ egg
60g flour
120ml cold water

YAMAIMO

Mountain Yam

Strengthen the stomach

Frequent urination
Stamina
Weak stomach
Asthma
Good circulation

BASICS

You Can Stomach it !

Yamaimo aid the absorption of carbohydrates, which then aid the absorption of other nutrients. It is very good for improving your general health especially following periods of illness. It is particularly good for weak stomach conditions, bowel troubles, over urination, fatigue and those suffering a loss of stamina.

NUTRITION & HEALING

Fresh and Raw

For diarrhoea, simmer some mountain yam, eat it, and also drink the simmered water. This yam can be eaten raw and since overcooking will inhibit the digestive enzymes, using the yam in fresh salads is one of the best ways of making the most of its vitamins and minerals, and its healing properties.

TASTE & USE Young Mountain Yams

Yamaimo can taste bitter, so it is advisable to soak them in vinegared water before using; this applies to eating them raw or as preparation for cooking. They are best bought in late autumn or early winter. Choose the lighter coloured ones as these will be younger; choose those that are heavy and fat but not too long. Don't handle the vegetable too much as it might cause your hands to itch. Wrap them in newspaper to store.

FACTS

per 100g YAMAIMO

Vitamin B$_1$	0.1mg	Cholesterol	0.0mg
Vitamin C	6.0mg	Dietary fibre	1.0g
Calcium	17.0mg	Glucose	13.5g
Calories	65.0kcal	Iron	0.4mg
Carbohydrate	13.8g	Potassium	500mg

RECIPE

Mountain Yam Salad
yamaimo salada

Cut the mountain yam into very fine strips. Mix the sugar, vinegar and salt and use it to dress the yam. Slice the nori into small pieces and use it to garnish the salad.
Side dish.

Ingredients (Serves 4)

1/3 mountain yam
1 tbsp sugar
3 tbsp vinegar
1/2 tsp salt
1 sheet *nori*

**nori = sheet dried seaweed
(1 sheet - 21cm x 19 cm)*

KONNYAKU

— Devil's Tongue Jelly —

Control the calories

Weight problems
Constipation
Diabetes
Stomach ache
Discharging waste

BASICS

Weight Watch

Konnyaku is a type of jelly usually made from the root or bulb of the devil's tongue plant, *amorphollus konjak*. As konnyaku contains almost no calories it is a good healthy option for the weight conscious. It can also be helpful in treating diabetes and constipation.

NUTRITION & HEALING

Waste Control

This vegetarian jelly has a lot of dietary fibre making it good for discharging waste from the body. It contains a specific type of dietary fibre that continues working for longer and assists in removing more waste. Konnyaku has a great capacity for cleansing. For stomach ache, wrap a block of simmered konnyaku in a towel and whilst the konnyaku is still warm place it on the stomach to soothe.

TASTE & USE

Subtlety

Konnyaku has an extremely subtle taste, one that has to be acquired over time. It tends to be included in cooking for its low calorie content and health properties as much as for its flavour. It is normally sold packaged in a type of limewater which prevents it from gathering bacteria, so whilst storing it, leave it in this water. Rinse it in fresh water just before using. It is best to slice konnyaku up finely as this helps it to absorb other flavours during cooking.

FACTS

per 100g KONNYAKU

Calcium	43.0mg	Fat	0.0g
Calories	5.0kcal	Iron	0.4mg
Carbohydrate	2.3g	Phosphorus	5.0mg
Cholesterol	0.0mg	Potassium	60.0mg
Dietary fibre	2.2g	Protein	0.1g

RECIPE

Red Hot Devil's Tongue
piri-kara konnyaku

Rinse the konnyaku and cut it into bite size pieces. Stir-fry the konnyaku well. Mix the sauce ingredients, add the sauce to the stir-fry and cook until the sauce is reduced to nothing. Sprinkle with red-hot chilli peppers. Garnish with sesame seeds. *Side dish.*

Ingredients (Serves 4)
500g konnyaku,
2 tbsp vegetable oil
some finely sliced red-hot chilli pepper
some sesame seeds

Sauce
240ml *dashi*
2 tbsp soy sauce
3 tbsp sugar
2 tbsp sake
1 tbsp *mirin*

*dashi = Japanese soup stock
*mirin = sweet cooking sake

DAIZU

Soya beans

Enhance your memory

Senility
Alzheimer's
High blood pressure
Diabetes
Arteriosclerosis

BASICS ## Memory Matters

The specific type of protein present in soya beans is good for improving the memory, and daizu have long been associated with the prevention of the onset of senility and Alzheimer's disease. Soya beans are also beneficial in helping prevent arteriosclerosis, diabetes and high blood pressure. They are extremely rich in minerals, especially phosphorus, iron and calcium.

NUTRITION & HEALING ## Reduce Cholesterol

The protein in soya beans is good for reducing the cholesterol level and therefore protects the heart and circulatory system. Soya beans contain the same amount of protein, by weight, as meat but obviously contain much less fat. Since the beans encourage good circulation, they are of benefit to your general health and also promote good skin condition.

TASTE & USE

Spirited Beans

It is best to choose shiny beans that have a clear shape. When storing soya beans it is advisable to avoid both damp places and sunlight.

In Japan soya beans are thought of as the 'meat of the earth' and are highly valued for their nutrition. Legend also has it that soya beans can repel or even remove devils or evil spirits.

FACTS

per 100g DAIZU

Vitamin B₁	0.83mg	Dietary fibre	17.1g
Calcium	240.0mg	Glucose	23.7g
Calories	417.0kcal	Iron	9.4mg
Carbohydrate	28.2g	Protein	35.3g
Cholesterol	0.0mg	Phosphorus	580.0mg

RECIPE

Simmered Soya Beans with Vegetables
daizu no nimono

Cook the soya beans in water. Cut all the vegetables into small pieces and then add them to the drained soya beans and simmer in the soup stock until tender. Add the remaining liquid ingredients and cook gently for 10min or until the sauce is reduced to nothing. *Side dish.*

Ingredients (Serves 4)

150g soya beans
20cm sheet kelp
½ carrot
½ lotus root
2 shiitake

500ml *dashi*
80ml soy sauce
3 tbsp *mirin*
2 tbsp sake

*dashi = Japanese soup stock
*mirin = sweet cooking sake

TOFU

Tofu

Youthful complexion

Anti-ageing
Clear skin
Brain stimulant
Arteriosclerosis
Bowel trouble

Youthful Looks

As well as being a good food for alleviating the symptoms of bowel troubles, a weak stomach and fatigue, tofu aids further absorption of vitamin E and is most highly regarded for its effects on the skin. Tofu encourages a good, clear complexion and has many of the benefits of soya beans but in a more easily digested form. If you've ever wondered at the secret of Japanese youthful appearance, tofu is probably one of the main answers.

Longer Life

Tofu making has a history of at least 2,000 years and has been closely linked with healthy longevity in both Japan and China. It is an incredibly easy food for the body to metabolise making it a good food to include after a period of ill health, or as a food for children and the elderly. It is also believed to help alleviate the effects of the menopause.

TASTE & USE

Fresh Tofu

Tofu though subtle, varies in taste along with the differences in its texture. It is produced all year round and can therefore be bought in any season. Be careful to note the 'sell by' and 'use by' dates, and while storing it in the fridge make sure that you change the water that it is in daily (use fresh, cold water). Tofu is rich in protein, calcium, iron and phosphorus.

FACTS

per 100g TOFU (Kinugoshi)

Vitamin B₁	0.1mg	Cholesterol	0.0mg
Vitamin E	0.2mg	Iron	1.1mg
Calcium	90.0mg	Phosphorus	65.0mg
Calories	58.0kcal	Potassium	140.0mg
Carbohydrate	1.7g	Protein	5.0g

RECIPE

Chilled Tofu
hiyayakko

Slice the spring onion and myoga very finely and grate the ginger. Lay the tofu on a plate garnished with the spring onion, myoga and ginger, and serve with soy sauce. *Light dish.*

Ingredients (Serves 1)

140g tofu
¼ spring onion
½ *myoga*
small piece fresh ginger
soy sauce

*myoga = Japanese ginger

NATTO

— Fermented Soya Beans —

Stroke prevention

Stroke
Sinusitis
Heart problems
Sexual potency
Degenerative brain disorders

Avoid strokes

Natto is made from soya beans and therefore has the same basic properties, but rather like tofu, it is more easily digested and absorbed. The fermenting process the beans undergo, increases their vitamin B_2 content sixfold and this is fundamental to their role in helping avoid strokes, arteriosclerosis and myocardial infarction. The fermented beans are also thought to prevent degenerative brain disorders.

*NUTRITION
& HEALING*

Sexual Potency

The fermenting process provides the soya beans with further properties, and one of these is that it increases sexual potency. This makes it perfect for anyone seeking a natural alternative to 'Viagra'. Natto is also beneficial in relieving sinusitis, heart problems and constipation. Natto is rich in enzymes and is very good for digestion.

TASTE & USE

Intense Aroma !

Perhaps the smell of natto is more noteworthy than the taste, as it is famed for its extremely pungent fermented smell, that said it is a taste and aroma worth acquiring as it is such a nutritious and healing food. It can be bought all year round and is best eaten within 2-3 days. Store it in a cool, dry place. Its nutritional value is increased when eaten with raw egg and it is popularly eaten like this in Japan.

FACTS

per 100g NATTO

Vitamin B$_2$	0.56mg	Dietary fibre	6.7g
Calcium	90.0mg	Fat	10.0g
Calories	200.0kcal	Glucose	9.8g
Carbohydrate	12.1g	Iron	3.3mg
Cholesterol	0.0mg	Protein	16.5g

RECIPE

Squid with Natto
ika no natto ae

Slice the squid into narrow strips. Combine the natto with the egg yolk and soy sauce and mix well. Mix the raw squid with the sauce and garnish with finely chopped chives. *Side dish.*

Ingredients (Serves 1)

100g squid
a few chives

Sauce
50g (1 packet) natto
1 egg yolk
soy sauce

MISO

— Fermented Soya Bean Paste —

Remove nicotine and alcohol

Liver cancer
Bowel cancer
Stomach cancer
Hangover
High blood pressure

BASICS   # Kill Nicotine and Alcohol

Miso is a very beneficial food; made from soya beans it obviously has many of the same positive attributes, and rather like natto is very easy for the system to digest. A particular feature of miso is its capacity to help rid the body of some of the harmful toxins it is exposed to, and these include both nicotine and alcohol.

NUTRITION & HEALING   # Liver Protection

Miso has a high vitamin E content and when vitamins A and C are present is very beneficial in both cleansing the body, and in various cancer prevention. Of note is its role in the prevention of liver, stomach and bowel cancers.

As miso removes harmful elements from the body and helps to protect the liver, it is good for those recovering from alcohol abuse. It is also good at reducing high blood pressure.

TASTE & USE

Tasty Miso

Miso comes in many varieties and each has a wonderful savoury taste. Be guided by the 'sell by' date, it can be kept refrigerated for quite some time, but be careful it doesn't turn - if it develops an acid taste, or an overpowering smell then it is past its best. It won't last if it is exposed to the air.

FACTS

per 100g MISO (Kome, aka miso)

Vitamin E	0.9mg	Dietary fibre	4.1g
Calcium	130.0mg	Iron	4.3mg
Calories	186.0kcal	Phosphorus	200.0mg
Carbohydrate	21.1g	Potassium	440.0mg
Cholesterol	0.0mg	Protein	13.1g

RECIPE

Miso Soup with Tofu
tofu no misoshiru

Cube the tofu, 1.5cm. Slice the spring onion finely. Heat the soup stock for 3-4min and gently dissolve the miso in it. Add the tofu, heat gently (don't allow it to boil). Garnish with spring onion. *Side dish.*

Ingredients (Serves 4)

140g tofu
40g miso
1 spring onion
1 litre *dashi*

*dashi = Japanese soup stock

SOBA

— Buckwheat Noodles —

Lower your blood pressure

High blood pressure
Constipation
Digestion
Arteriosclerosis
Circulation

BASICS

Lower the Pressure !

Soba noodles are made from buckwheat. They mainly comprise of carbohydrate but a type that is easily digested and assimilated. There is an unusual amount of the rare vitamin P present, and this is good for strengthening capillaries and blood vessels and so helps prevent high blood pressure and stroke.

NUTRITION & HEALING

Energy Regain

Soba noodles are rich in vitamin B1 making them a good option for those recovering from stress and wanting to regain a decent energy level. Drinking the water that soba is cooked in is very good for you, as it will contain much of the noodles' vitamin P. For treating fever, bruising or burns, dampen a cloth with powdered soba mixed with warm water, and lay it on the affected area.

TASTE & USE

Healthy Noodles

Fresh soba noodles are preferable but the dried noodles are also beneficial to your health. Soba noodles should be cooked according to the instructions on the packet. Once cooked, the noodles should be rinsed well in cold water to remove their stickiness and drained. These noodles are eaten both hot and cold. Dried soba noodles can be kept for up to a year if stored away from damp.

FACTS

per 100g SOBA

Vitamin B$_1$	0.19mg	Dietary fibre	2.7g
Calcium	18.0mg	Fat	1.9g
Calories	274.0kcal	Iron	1.4mg
Carbohydrate	54.5g	Phosphorus	170.0mg
Cholesterol	0.0mg	Protein	9.8g

Chilled Soba
zaru soba

Transfer the soba to cold water after cooking to cool, drain, arrange on a plate and sprinkle with dried seaweed. Serve the cold soup in a deep bowl. The spring onion and wasabi are condiments to add to the soup before dipping the noodles. *Main dish.*

Ingredients (Serves 1)

100g soba noodles
some dried seaweed-
(finely cut)
⅔ spring onion-
(sliced finely)
some wasabi
150ml cold noodle soup

GENMAI

— (Unpolished) Brown Rice —

Stimulate the metabolism

Anti-ageing
Metabolism booster
Fatigue
Sexual health
Mental health

BASICS Metabolic Booster

Unpolished, brown rice contains four times the vitamin B1 and vitamin E content of polished, white rice; it also has three times the amount of dietary fibre. This rice is particularly good for boosting your metabolism as the vitamin B1 helps carbohydrates convert to energy efficiently. The dietary fibre is also good for keeping the bowels in good condition.

NUTRITION & HEALING Healthy Hair and Skin

Genmai contains particular elements that are effective in fighting the signs of ageing. As the rice stimulates the metabolism it naturally makes it a very good ingredient for improving the condition of hair and skin. It has a positive effect on both mental and sexual health, and is thought to counteract the harmful effects of pollution.

TASTE & USE

Good Digestion

This rice has a slightly nutty taste. Whenever possible choose organically grown brown rice. In Japan this rice is often cooked twice to make it softer and easier to digest. This rice should be chewed well to further assist digestion.

FACTS

per 100g GENMAI

Vitamin B₁	0.54mg	Cholesterol	0.0mg
Vitamin E	1.6mg	Dietary fibre	3.4g
Calcium	10.0mg	Iron	1.1mg
Calories	351.0kcal	Phosphorus	300.0mg
Carbohydrate	72.8g	Protein	7.4g

RECIPE

Brown Rice Porridge
genmai gayu

Wash the rice thoroughly then soak it in the water for 4 hours. Slice the shiitake finely. Bring the rice to a boil in the water, salt and soy sauce and then simmer for 35-40min. Add the shiitake, cook for a further 2 min then garnish with finely chopped chives. *Main dish.*

Ingredients (Serves 4)

150g brown rice
1.5 litres water
3 shiitake
1 tbsp soy sauce
1 tsp salt
a few chives

NUKA

Rice Bran

Attractive complexion

Skin problems
Healthy hair
Cancer
Immune System
Bowel trouble

BASICS

Youthful Skin

Nuka is closely associated with clear, smooth looking skin, and strong, healthy hair. It stimulates the metabolism and as such helps to cleanse the skin, keeping it renewed and youthful. Nuka can be used as a facial wash and can also be wrapped in a cloth and placed in the bath. In the past in Japan it was common to find restorative hair tonics, soaps and skincare products, which used nuka as their basic ingredient.

NUTRITION & HEALING

Bowels of the Bowels !

The type of dietary fibre present in nuka stimulates the action of bacteria in the bowel that work extremely well in cleansing the system. It also works to reduce cholesterol in the blood and rids the body of toxins. Rice bran also strengthens the immune system, especially against cancers and is a rich source of vitamins, minerals and of course, fibre.

TASTE & USE

Pickled

In Japan, nuka is most commonly used for making pickles. It can also be used by adding it to a drink such as tea or milk and may need to be sweetened; it doesn't taste very good by itself. Another way of including nuka in your diet is to cook it with minced meat.

FACTS

per 100g NUKA

Vitamin B1	2.5mg	Dietary fibre	7.8g
Vitamin B2	0.5mg	Fat	18.3g
Calcium	46.0mg	Glucose	38.3g
Calories	286.0kcal	Iron	6.0mg
Carbohydrate	46.1g	Protein	13.2g

RECIPE

Rice Bran Pickles
nuka zuke

Boil salt and water, reduce heat to 30℃ and mix with the nuka and yeast in a large bowl, knead it like bread dough until texture is even. Lay the kelp at the base of a large jar with a lid, add the nuka 'dough' and push the vegetables into it whole, covering them with 'dough'. Seal the lid and leave in a cool, dark place for 24hrs. Rinse pickles well and slice up to serve. *Side dish.*

Ingredients

3 litres water
250g sea salt
2kg nuka
300g natural yeast
20g kelp
1 aubergine
½ large cucumber
¼ daikon

*daikon = Japanese radish
*aubergine = eggplant

AZUKI

Azuki Beans

Sexual health and vitality

Water retention
Swelling
Alertness
Sexual Health
Asthma

BASICS

Sexual Vitality

Azuki contain a lot of vitamin B₁ which is good for converting carbohydrates to energy, and this makes the beans a good choice for anyone fighting to keep their finger on the pulse. As well as promoting alertness and increasing concentration, these beans are beneficial for sexual health, healthy skin and as an appetite stimulant.

NUTRITION & HEALING

Water Control

The nutrition in azuki aids the reduction of cholesterol, and works to control the water in the body. This makes it effective in water control, reducing swelling and removing alcohol from the system. To reduce swelling, simmer 30g of azuki beans in 600ml water and drink the water daily. Grated azuki mixed with the juice of *daikon* can be used on a wound to assist healing.

TASTE
& USE

Beans as Brain Food

The beans have a tendency to taste bitter, so it is advisable to change the water during cooking. These beans are full of complex carbohydrates, vitamins and minerals and have long been connected with encouraging mental agility and good concentration; perhaps that's another secret of Japanese success.

FACTS

per 100g AZUKI

Vitamin B₁	0.45mg	Dietary fibre	17.8g
Calcium	75.0mg	Iron	5.4mg
Calories	339.0kcal	Phosphorus	350.0mg
Carbohydrate	58.7g	Potassium	1500.0mg
Cholesterol	0.0mg	Protein	20.3g

RECIPE

Red Rice, Red Beans
sekihan

Wash the azuki beans and boil for 5min, drain. Add 500ml fresh water, boil, lower heat and cook until tender. Drain and reserve the water, allow to cool. Soak the rice in the bean-water for 1-2hours, drain once coloured. Steam the mixed rice and beans for 40min. Sprinkle with sesame salt. *Main dish.*

Ingredients (Serves 4)

450g glutinous rice
50g azuki beans
1 litre water
pinch of black sesame salt

GOMA

Sesame

Forget going grey

Greying hair
Stress
Brittle bones
Arteriosclerocis
Anti-ageing

Ghostly Grey

Going grey isn't a problem for some, in fact it's often attractive, but for those who'd prefer not to, sesame is very good for the circulatory system and contains lots of vitamin E which together encourage the blood supply to the hair and skin. This helps them to retain their colour and good condition. 50% of sesame is made up of unsaturated fatty acids that are good at reducing cholesterol. Goma is also good for brittle bones, headaches, high blood pressure, and arteriosclerosis.

NUTRITION
& HEALING

Calm

Sesame is noticeably beneficial in reducing stress and irritability; it has a very calming effect on the body and mind. Simmer sesame in water and take it as a daily drink. This drink is also good for treating dry skin conditions.

Sesame Season

The toasted sesame seeds are very aromatic and the black seeds are thought to have stronger health related properties than the white ones. Sesame seeds and oil can be bought all year round. Sesame seeds are a common ingredient in Japanese recipes and are often included as garnish.

FACTS

per 100g GOMA

Vitamin B₁	0.95mg		Cholesterol	0.0mg
Vitamin B₂	0.25mg		Dietary fibre	13.2g
Calcium	1200.0mg		Glucose	15.3g
Calories	578.0kcal		Iron	9.6mg
Carbohydrate	18.4g		Protein	19.8g

RECIPE

Spinach with Sesame
hourensou no goma ae

Boil the spinach with a pinch of salt, then rinse in cold water and drain. Slice the spinach into 3cm strips and toss in the soy sauce. Grind the sesame seeds, mix the sauce ingredients and then use to dress the spinach. *Side dish.*

Ingredients (Serves 4)

100g spinach
1 tbsp soy sauce

Sauce
2 tbsp white sesame seeds
1.5 tbsp soy sauce
1 tbsp sugar

KONBU

Kelp

Feel revitalised

Liver complaints
Hair Loss
Gum disease
Heartburn
High blood pressure

BASICS

Revitalise !

Kelp is incredibly rich in vitamins and minerals and therefore has many health related properties. It contains a lot of iodine which is very effective in increasing your energy level and giving you that revived feeling, especially necessary in the winter months when there's a lack of sunshine. It also contains a lot of potassium, which is effective in lowering blood pressure. Konbu is also used to treat liver complaints, swelling and anaemia.

NUTRITION & HEALING

Heartless Heartburn

When you soak konbu in water you will notice a stickiness, this contains a certain type of acid that is helpful in reducing cholesterol. For heartburn, grill some dried konbu and then eat it. If you grill konbu until it is burnt and then make it into a powder, this is effective in treating gum disease. One 10cm x 10cm sheet of konbu cut up and soaked in water overnight provides a drink that is good at reducing hair loss. This should be drunk daily.

TASTE & USE

Konbu King

Konbu has a light, slightly salty seaweed flavour. It is very highly rated for its health benefits and as a rich source of nourishment. In Japan it is commonly used in the Japanese soup stock: *dashi*. When you buy kelp it comes in dried sheets, don't be put off by the white powder on the surface, this has a lot of taste and is basically a natural food enhancer, hence its inclusion in many Japanese fish dishes – it really is a super complement to seafood.

FACTS

per 100g KONBU

Vitamin A	560.0IU	Carbohydrate	61.5g
Vitamin B₁	0.48mg	Glucose	58.2g
Vitamin C	25.0mg	Iron	3.9mg
Calcium	710.0mg	Potassium	6100.0mg
Calories	145.0kcal	Protein	8.2g

RECIPE

Konbu Rolls (fish)
konbu maki

Soak the konbu until soft, 10-20min. Wash gourd in salt water and simmer for 3-4min. Spread the tuna thinly over the sheet of konbu and roll up, tie the rolls with gourd ribbon at 2 points. Boil the rolls in a pan with A, add the soy sauce and ginger juice, and simmer for 10-15min. Cut the rolls in half.
Light dish.

Ingredients (Serves 4)

6 sheets konbu (20cm x 15cm)
20g gourd –
(cut into ribbons)
300g tinned tuna

A 600ml *dashi*
1 ½ tbsp sugar
50ml sake

3 tbsp soy sauce
1-2 tbsp juice grated ginger

*dashi = Japanese soup stock

Wakame (Seaweed)

Avoid hardened arteries

Sinusitis
Hardening of the arteries
Diabetes
Weight problems
Goitre

BASICS   Hard Hearted

This variety of seaweed is very beneficial in treating hardening of the arteries and contains potassium, which is good for lowering blood pressure. It is also good for treating asthma, sinusitis and irritability, indeed irritability often accompanies a very bad sinus headache ! Other conditions that it is effective in treating include diabetes, hair loss, and constipation.

NUTRITION & HEALING   Blood Cleansing

Wakame is rich in vitamins and minerals and has a high iodine content. Amongst other things, iodine is good for controlling metabolism, and the minerals cleanse the blood. The effectiveness of this iodine is doubled when the seaweed is eaten with oil. And when wakame is eaten with vinegar it is of benefit in reducing cholesterol, the natural thing to do is to eat it with salad dressing.

TASTE & USE   The Wonders of Wakame

It can be said that Japan prides itself on its history of good health and at least some of this can be attributed to its love of various seaweed. Wakame is most commonly eaten in soups and salads in Japan. It has a light seaweed flavour, is dark green in colour, and it is usual to buy it dried, reconstituting it with water when necessary. It is worth noting that over boiling will reduce the vitamin and mineral content.

FACTS

per 100g WAKAME

Vitamin A	780.0IU	Dietary fibre	5.5g
Vitamin B_2	0.18mg	Glucose	3.8g
Vitamin C	15.0mg	Iron	0.7mg
Calcium	100.0mg	Protein	1.9g
Carbohydrate	4.2g	Potassium	730.0mg

RECIPE

Wakame Soup
wakame supu

Wash the wakame and shiitake and cut into bite-size pieces. Boil up the soup stock, add the wakame, salt and soy sauce, stir gently and it's ready to serve. Garnish with sesame seeds and finely chopped chives. *Light dish.*

Ingredients (Serves 4)

50g wakame
2 shiitake
1 litre *dashi*
1 tsp soy sauce
a few chives
a few white sesame
seeds
pinch of salt

*dashi = Japanese soup stock

Nori (Dried Seaweed)

Lung repair and protection

Lung cancer
Hair loss
Constipation
Mental fatigue
Irritability

BASICS

Lung Repair

For anyone attempting to protect their lungs in smoke filled environments, and for those who have given up smoking and want to increase the health of damaged lungs, nori is a useful ingredient. This seaweed helps stop harmful tar from attaching itself to the lungs. It is also effective in the prevention of certain cancers, especially of the lungs and bowels, and is helpful in treating conditions of anaemia, hair loss and greying hair.

NUTRITION & HEALING

Quit Being Irritable !

This seaweed is rich in vitamin B1, which encourages carbohydrates' effective conversion to energy, making it useful for anyone fighting mental fatigue. It also contains a lot of calcium and this is excellent for reducing feelings of irritability. Vitamin C is often lost when heated but the vitamin C in nori is more resilient to heat.

Crisp Seaweed

This seaweed comes in dried sheets, and has a distinctive, fresh, crisp taste. It is popularly eaten as the wrapping for sushi and for the rice balls called onigiri, and as garnish for many Japanese dishes. It can be bought all year round; it is important to store it in a dry place.

FACTS

per 100g NORI

Vitamin A	13,000.0IU	Carbohydrate	43.6g
Vitamin B1	1.1mg	Fat	2.0g
Vitamin B2	3.2mg	Glucose	41.7g
Vitamin C	95.0mg	Iron	12.7mg
Calcium	410.0mg	Protein	40.9g

RECIPE

Thin Rolled Sushi
hoso-maki

Place the cooked rice in a flat-bottomed bowl. Mix the vinegar with the sugar and salt, add it to the rice and mix swiftly. Cut the cucumber into 8 - lengthways. Spread half the rice over a sheet of nori, lay the cucumber down the centre and roll up – preferably using a bamboo rolling mat. Repeat for the second sushi roll. Slice each roll into 4.
Light dish.

Ingredients (Makes 2 rolls)
2 × sheet nori
(11.5cm × 9.5cm)
140g sushi rice
25g cucumber
1 $\frac{1}{3}$ tbsp Japanese vinegar
$\frac{2}{3}$ tbsp sugar
$\frac{1}{4}$ tbsp salt

HIJIKI

Hijiki (Seaweed)

Boost your blood

Nervousness
Arteriosclerosis
Obesity
Bowel disorders
Anaemia

BASICS

Iron out Anaemia

Hijiki is very rich in iron, but whilst this is the case, the iron content of this seaweed isn't easily absorbed by the body. If, however, the seaweed is eaten with a high amount of vitamin C, then the body can take full advantage of this iron reserve. Hijiki is therefore best consumed with other vegetables. This iron is also beneficial to those with anaemia. Including hijiki in the diet can also help in the battles against arteriosclerosis and obesity.

NUTRITION & HEALING

Calmed Nerves

Many sea vegetables have similar properties, and like nori, hijiki has a calming effect on the nervous system; its high calcium content is very advantageous to those suffering from periods of nervousness or anxiety. Hijiki contains a lot of dietary fibre, which has a healthy effect on the bowels.

TASTE & USE

Healthy Hijiki

The hijiki variety of seaweed is more porous than others, and is the easiest to eat. It is almost black in colour, and its surface is less sticky than other seaweed. It is normally sold dried so it can be kept a long time if stored in a dry place. It is best to choose the shiniest looking hijiki. It is usually reconstituted with water before use.

FACTS

per 100g HIJIKI

Vitamin A	310.0IU	Fat	1.3g
Calcium	1,400.0mg	Glucose	47.0g
Carbohydrate	56.2g	Iron	55.0mg
Cholesterol	1.0mg	Magnesium	620.0mg
Dietary fibre	43.3g	Protein	10.6g

RECIPE

Simmered Seaweed with Vegetables
hijiki no nimono

Slice up the deep-fried bean curd, carrot and konnyaku and cook them in the dashi with the hijiki for 10min. Add the remaining ingredients and continue to simmer for 4min. *Side dish.*

Ingredients (Serves 4)

125g hijiki (reconstituted)
1 carrot
2 slices deep-fried
bean curd
125g konnyaku

250ml *dashi*
1 tbsp sugar
2 tbsp soy sauce
2 tbsp sake

*dashi = Japanese soup stock

KOMEZU

Rice Vinegar

Smoother skin

Skin problems
Stomach trouble
Fatigue
Antiseptic
Longevity

BASICS

Skin Clarity

In Japan, vinegar, and in particular, rice vinegar, has long been associated with longevity and with youthful looking skin. Part of the reason for this association is the fact that vinegar increases the potency of vitamin C, and this is effective in promoting a good complexion. As well as including rice vinegar in the diet, the Japanese were known to use it in cosmetic products for its favourable effects on the skin.

NUTRITION
& HEALING

Killing Power

Perhaps the strongest thing to note about vinegar is it ability to kill – germs. It is an incredible sterilising agent, effective as an antiseptic and anti-bacterial. Many known germs are killed after ten minutes exposure to vinegar, and this is why it is used in Japanese dishes that involve raw fish or meat. This property makes it a healthy dietary addition for anyone with bowel or stomach problems, and again its cleansing effect is of obvious benefit to the skin.

TASTE & USE

Full Colour

Kome-zu is a rather light tasting vinegar. There are two types of komezu; one is fermented naturally over two to three years, and this is very expensive. A drop of this vinegar will help capture and retain the colour of vegetables if added to the water during cooking. Having a vinegar bottle open whilst cooking meat will help to remove the strong smell.

FACTS

per 100g KOME-ZU

Vitamin C	0.0mg	Dietary fibre	0.0g
Calcium	2.0mg	Fat	0.0g
Calories	32.0kcal	Glucose	5.0g
Carbohydrate	5.0g	Iron	0.1mg
Cholesterol	0.0mg	Protein	0.2g

RECIPE

Radish & Carrot Vinegared Salad
daikon to ninjin no sunomono

Slice the radish and carrot finely, sprinkle them with salt and then rinse them under water and drain. Mix the dressing ingredients and add to the salad. *Side dish.*

Ingredients (Serves 4)

200g radish
60g carrot
pinch of salt

Dressing
4 tbsp komezu
4 tbsp sugar

RYOKuCHA

Green Tea

Allergic reaction

Allergies
Hay fever
Colds
Flu
Cancer prevention

BASICS

Allergy Alert

Japanese green tea is good for treating allergies, particularly hay fever. Ryokucha is believed to be cancer preventative and to have a positive effect on the immune system. Its high vitamin content also make it helpful in treating colds and flu.

NUTRITION & HEALING

Ageless

This tea is very good for the skin and contains anti-ageing properties. It is also good for bad breath.

FACTS
per 100g RYOKUCHA

Vitamin A	7200.0IU
Vitamin B2	1.4mg
Vitamin C	250.0mg

Published by: Cross Media Ltd.
13 Berners Street, London W1T 3LH, UK
Tel: 020-7436-1960   Fax: 020-7436-1930

Copyright of Photography and Text © Cross Media Ltd. 2001

Project Manager: Kazuhiro Marumo
Author/Editor: J.L.Rollinson
Designer: Misa Watanabe
Photographer: Shinichi Sakai
Illustration: Osamu Miyagi
Calligraphy: Sumire Kakiuchi
DTP Production: Mutsumi Kawasaki, Kaori Tanimoto
Chef: Yoshiko Ito

ISBN 1-897701-92-6
Printed in Japan